Broken for you

**A setting for Holy Communion for congregation
with optional choir and instrumental parts**

Margaret **Rizza**

Kevin
Mayhew

We hope you enjoy *Broken for you*. Further copies are available
from your local Kevin Mayhew stockist.

In case of difficulty, please contact the publisher direct by writing to:

The Sales Department
KEVIN MAYHEW LTD
Buxhall
Stowmarket
Suffolk IP14 3BW

Phone 01449 737978
Fax 01449 737834
E-mail info@kevinmayhewltd.com

Please ask for our complete catalogue of outstanding Church Music.

First published in Great Britain in 2001 by Kevin Mayhew Ltd.

© Copyright 2001 Kevin Mayhew Ltd.

ISBN 1 84003 776 8
ISMN M 57004 899 1
Catalogue No: 1450221

1 2 3 4 5 6 7 8 9

Cover design by Jonathan Stroulger

Music setter: Geoffrey Moore
Proof reader: Marian Hellen

Printed and bound in Great Britain

Foreword

This setting may be performed by whatever voices and instruments you have available.

It can be sung in unison or with a choir, accompanied by organ alone or any number of instruments.

The congregation (for whom a photocopiable part is given on page 60) sing the melody throughout except in one or two places which are indicated in the score.

We would like to thank the following people for their performances on the enclosed CD:

Voices
Honor Mason   Soprano solo
Diana Campbell   Alto solo
Mark Holmes   Baritone solo
Paul Plumbley   Speaker
St Thomas' Music Group

Instrumentalists
Ian Davies   Flute
Daniel Weatherley   Violin
Nancy Sergeant   Oboe
Catharine Brooker   Cello
Paul Dean   Organ

Conducted by Margaret Rizza

Recorded in St Thomas' Church, Sevenoaks, Kent, by B&H Sound Services Ltd.

for St Thomas' Music Group

BROKEN FOR YOU

**A setting for Holy Communion for congregation
with optional choir and instrumental parts**

Margaret Rizza

KYRIE

Lord have mer - cy, Lord have mer - cy, Lord have mer - cy,

Lord have mer - cy, mer - cy

* *Small notes to be played only
if there is no solo instrument.*

KYRIE

Cello (Basso Continuo)

KYRIE

GLORIA

Glo - ry to God in the high - est, glo - ry to God on high; and

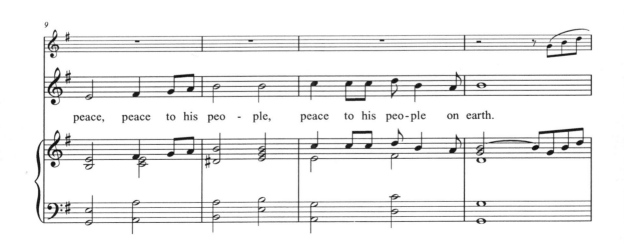

peace, peace to his peo - ple, peace to his peo - ple on earth.

Lord God, hea - ven - ly King, al - migh - ty God and

Fa - ther, we wor - ship you, we give you thanks, we

praise you for your glo - ry. Glo - ry to God in the

high - est and peace to his peo - ple on earth.

Lord Je-sus Christ, on-ly Son of the Fa - ther, Lord God, Lamb of God,

you take a-way the sin of the world, have mer - cy, have mer - cy on us.

Congregation

You are seat-ed at the right hand of the Fa - ther, re - ceive our prayer, re-

You are seat-ed at the right hand of the Fa - ther, re - ceive our prayer, re-

Instrument

ceive our prayer.

ceive our prayer.

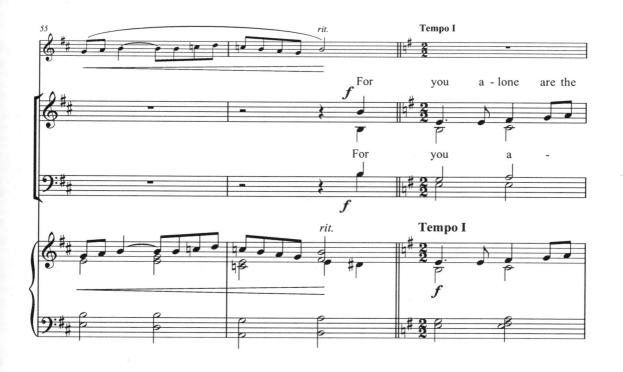

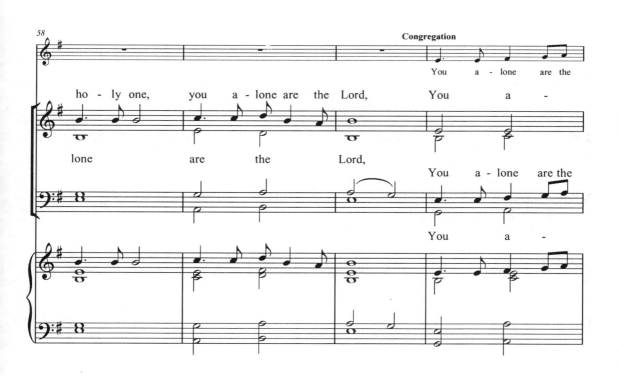

15

Christ with the Ho - ly Spi - rit, in the

glo - ry, the glo - ry, the glo - ry of the

cresc.

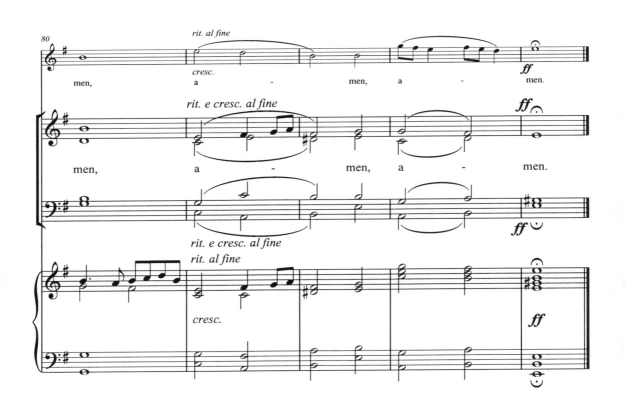

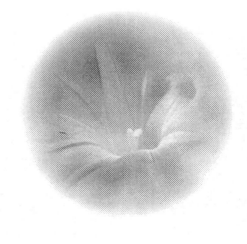

GLORIA

GLORIA

GLORIA

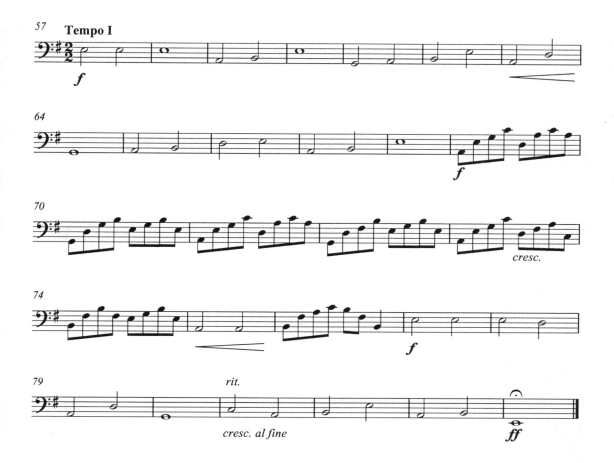

GOSPEL ACCLAMATION

Al - le - lu - ia, al - le - lu - ia,

al - le - lu - ia, al - le - lu - ia.

Verse. Example I

I am the light of the world, says the Lord. Who - e - ver fol - lows me

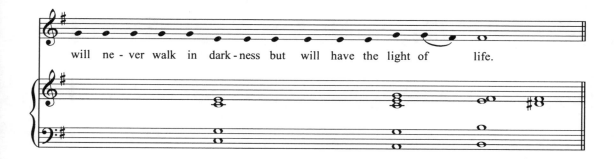

will ne - ver walk in dark - ness but will have the light of life.

Verse. Example II

Come, Ho - ly Spi - rit, fill the hearts of your faith - ful peo - ple

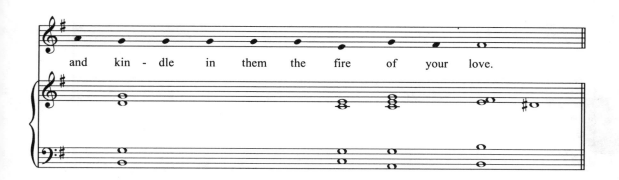

and kin - dle in them the fire of your love.

GOSPEL ACCLAMATION

Mosso (♩ = 72)

OPTIONAL CODA

* *A verse follows the first 12 bars, immediately preceding the instrumental entry.*

GOSPEL ACCLAMATION

Mosso ($\half = 72$)

Verse. Example I

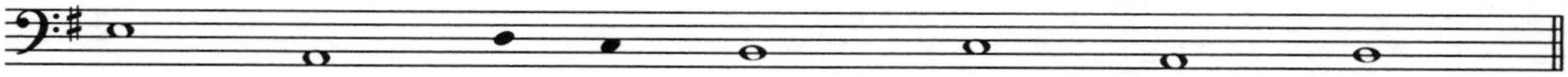

Verse. Example II

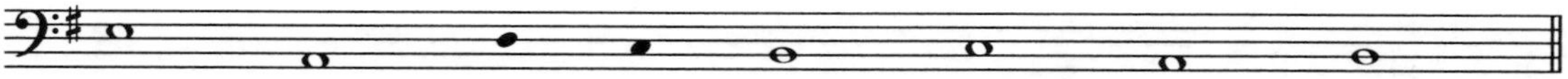

OPTIONAL CODA

SANCTUS

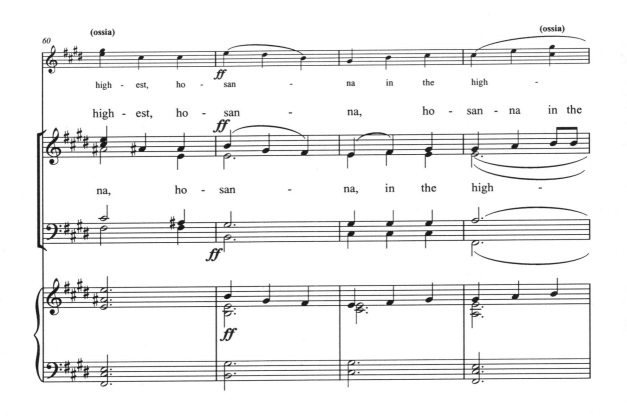

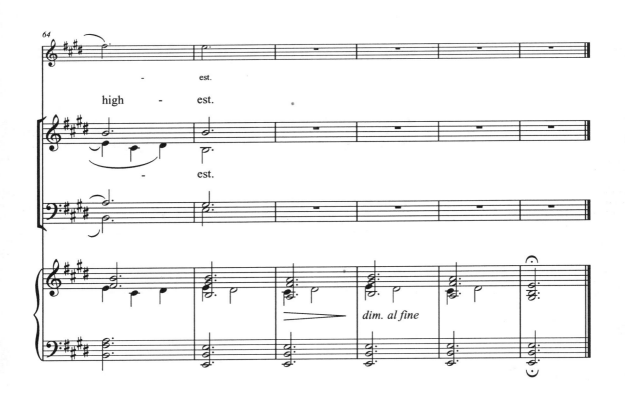

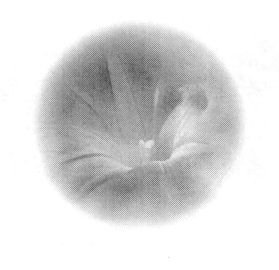

SANCTUS

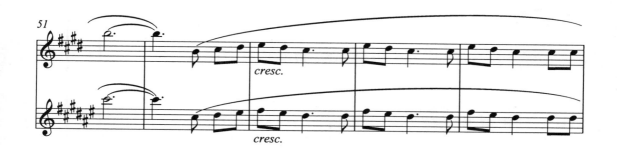

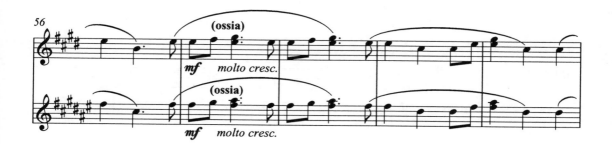

SANCTUS

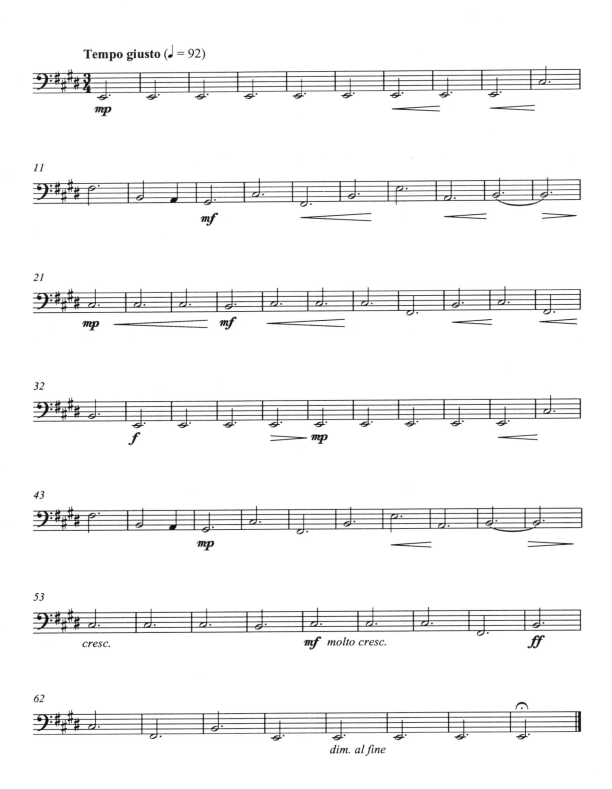

ACCLAMATIONS
1

Tempo giusto

President

Let us pro - claim the mys - t'ry of faith.

All

Christ has died, Christ is ri - sen; Christ has died, Christ is ri - sen, Christ, Christ will come a - gain.

Tempo giusto

President

Let us pro - claim the mys - t'ry of faith.

All

When we eat this bread, when we drink this cup, we pro - claim your death Lord Je - sus, un - til you come in glo - ry.

Cello (Basso Continuo)

ACCLAMATIONS
1, 2 and 4

Tempo giusto

3

Tempo giusto

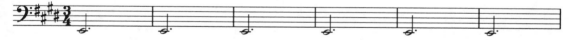

THE LORD'S PRAYER

Throughout this setting the words 'Holy be thy name' are sung by the choir alone. They do not appear in the congregation's part.

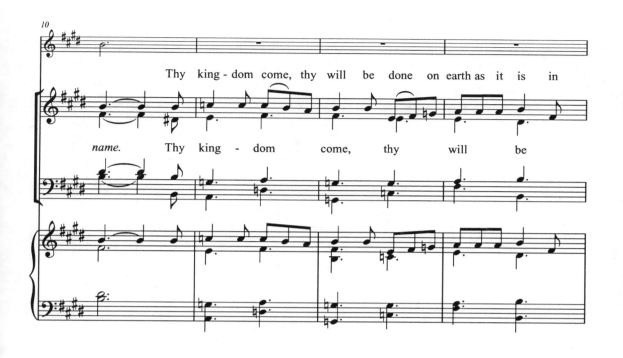

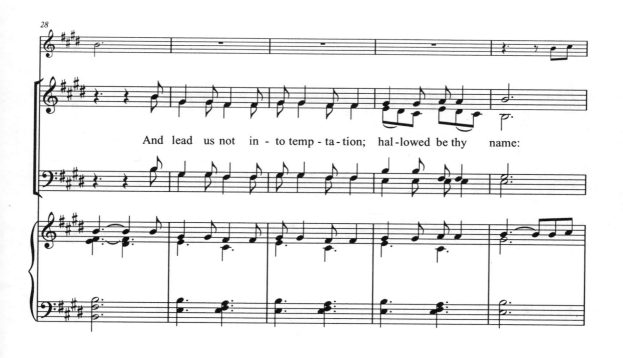

And lead us not in - to temp - ta - tion; hal - lowed be thy name:

But de - liv - er us from e - vil, de-

ho - ly be thy name. But de - li - ver us from

THE LORD'S PRAYER

Moderato (♩. = 63)

C instrument

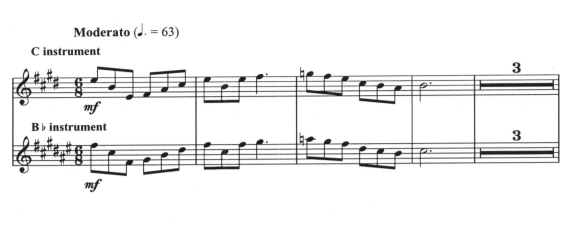

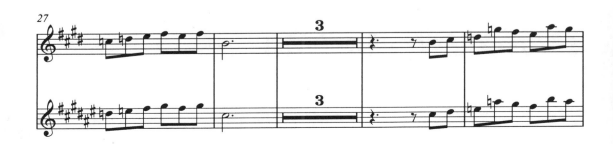

Cello (Basso Continuo)

THE LORD'S PRAYER

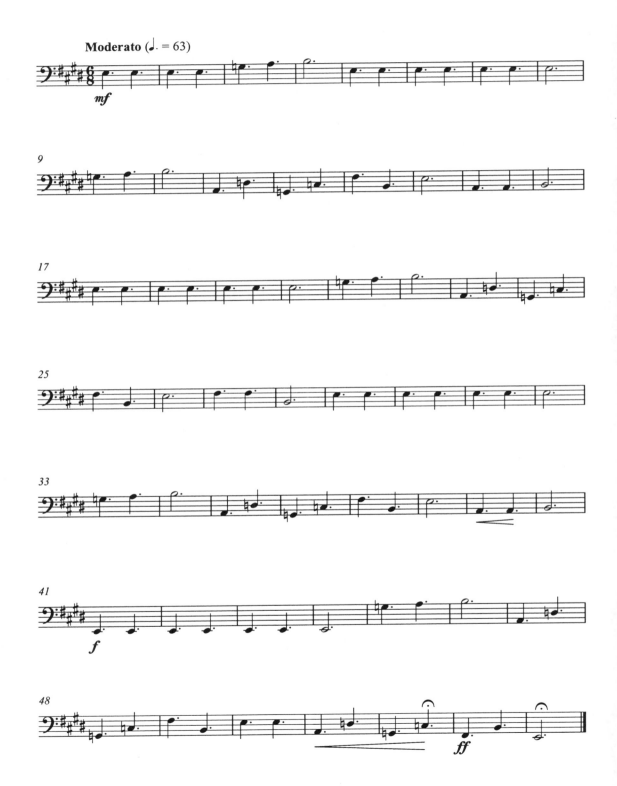

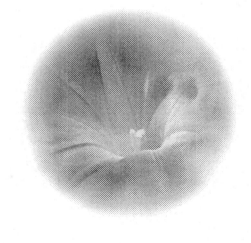

AGNUS DEI

* to be played when there is no solo instrument

Accompaniment with instrument

Accompaniment without instrument